# It's fun to draw
# Pirates
### Mark Bergin

*Author:*
**Mark Bergin** was born in Hastings, England. He has illustrated an award-winning series and written over twenty books. He has done many book designs, layouts and storyboards in many styles including cartoon for numerous books, posters and adverts. He lives in Bexhill-on-sea with his wife and three children.

*Editorial Assistant:*
Victoria England

**HOW TO USE THIS BOOK:**
Start by following the numbered splats on the left hand page. These steps will ask you to add some lines to your drawing. The new lines are always drawn in red so you can see how the drawing builds from step to step. Read the 'You can do it!' splats to learn about drawing and colouring techniques you can use.

Published in Great Britain in MMXII by Scribblers, a division of Book House
25 Marlborough Place, Brighton BN1 1UB
**www.salariya.com**
**www.book-house.co.uk**

ISBN-13: 978-1-908177-61-2

1 3 5 7 9 8 6 4 2

A CIP catalogue record for this book is available from the British Library.

Printed and bound in China.

PAPER FROM
SUSTAINABLE
**FORESTS**

Visit our website at **www.book-house.co.uk**
or go to **www.salariya.com** for **free** electronic versions of:
**You Wouldn't Want to be an Egyptian Mummy!**
**You Wouldn't Want to be a Roman Gladiator!**
**You Wouldn't Want to be a Polar Explorer!**
**You Wouldn't Want to Sail on a 19th-Century Whaling Ship!**

Visit our Bookhouse100 channel to see Mark Bergin doing step by step illustrations:

**www.youtube.com/user/bookhouse100**

# Contents

# Barnacle Boris

**1** Start with an oval for the head, add a line and ears.

**2** Add a hat, nose, mouth, eyes and eyebrows.

**3** Draw in the body. Add two lines for the waistcoat.

**4** Draw in the trousers, belt and feet.

**Splat-a-fact!**
Pirates used guns and swords as weapons.

**5** Draw in arms holding a pistol and a sword.

4

# Sharktooth Jack

**1** Draw in the head shape with dots for the eyes. Add a line for the headscarf.

## you can do it!

Use a wax crayon to draw the clouds. To add texture paint over with watercolour paint. Use a felt-tip for the lines.

**2** Draw in the eyebrows and mouth. Add dots for stubble and a knotted headscarf.

**3** Draw in the body.

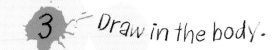

## splat-a-fact!

Pirates buried their treasure on desert islands.

**4** Add ragged trousers and legs.

**5** Draw in the arms and hands. Draw in the spade.

# Redbeard

**1** Draw in the head shape. Add a line for the headscarf.

**2** Draw in the beard and eyepatch. Add dots for the eye and mouth.

**3** Draw in a circle for the body. Add a belt and waistcoat.

**4** Draw in two arms and a lit match.

**You can do it!**
Use a graphite pencil for the lines and coloured inks to add colour.

**5**  Draw in ragged trousers and add the feet.

**Splat-a-fact!**
Pirate ships had cannons to shoot at their enemies with.

8

# Scurvy Jim

**1** Draw in the head shape. Add a line for the headscarf.

**2** Draw a dot for the eye. Add the mouth, ear, hair and knotted headscarf.

**3** Draw in the body shape and add a belt and waistcoat.

**Splat-a-fact!**
Pirate treasure is kept in a wooden chest.

**4** Draw in the arms carrying a treasure chest and sword.

**5** Draw in ragged trousers and add the feet.

10

11

# squid lips Sid

**you can do it!**
Place your paper over different surfaces and use colour pencils to create interesting textures. Use a felt-tip for the lines.

● Start with the head shape and draw a line for the headscarf.

● Add dots for eyes. Draw in the eyebrows, an ear and the knotted headscarf.

Add the body, arms and hands.

● Draw in the torn trousers and feet.

● Draw in the belt and broom.

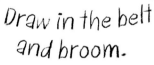

12

# starboard Steve

 **1** Start with the head shape. Draw in a line for the headscarf.

 **3** Add a box-shaped body and two lines for the waistcoat.

**2** Draw in the eyes, mouth and hair. Add an ear, an earring and a knotted headscarf.

**Splat-a-fact!**

'X' marks the spot on a treasure map where the treasure is buried.

**4** Draw in torn trousers and add feet.

**5** Draw in the arms holding a treasure map. Add a neckerchief.

14

You can do it!
Use felt-tip for the lines.
Add colour using oil
pastels. Blend or smudge
with your fingers.

15

# Monkey

splat-a-fact!
Pirates often had
pet monkeys.

**1** Draw two overlapping circles for the head. Add the hairline.

**2** Draw in dots for the eyes and nostrils. Add mouth and ears.

**3** Draw in the body. Add a headscarf.

you can do it!
Cut out strips of corrugated cardboard for the rope and stick down torn tissue paper for the background.

**4** Draw in torn trousers and add the monkey's legs and feet.

**5** Add arms and a long tail. Draw circles for fingers.

# Captain Clunk

**1** Start by cutting out this shape for the pirate's jacket. Stick down.

**2** Cut out the face shape. Stick down. Use a felt-tip to draw in buttons, hair, a nose and an eyepatch.

**you can do it!**

As you cut out each shape from coloured paper or tin foil, stick it down.

**3** Cut out the pirate's hat and beard from black paper. Stick down. Cut out a boot and a peg leg from brown paper. Stick down.

**4** Cut out the sword from tin foil and stick down. Cut out hands and stick down. Cut a crutch from brown paper and stick down.

18

splat-a-fact!
Some pirates had
wooden legs.

19

# Sophie Storm

**1** Start with a circle for the head. Add a nose, mouth and eyes.

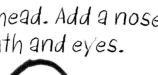

**2** Draw in a hat and hair.

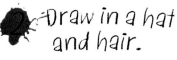

**3** Draw in a box-shaped body. Add sleeves.

## you can do it!

Use a brown felt-tip for the lines and add colour with coloured pencil crayons.

**4** Draw in circles for the hands holding a sword and dagger. Add belts and buckles.

## Splat-a-fact!

Sometimes girls were pirates too!

**5** Add the trousers and the feet.

# One-eyed John

**1** Start with an oval for the head. Add ears.

**you can do it!**
Use a felt-tip for the lines. Add ink washes then add a second coloured ink on top of an area that is still wet for extra effects.

**2** Draw in a headscarf. Add a nose, a dot for the eye, an eyepatch and a dagger between his teeth.

**3** Draw in a box-shaped body. Add a waistcoat and buckle.

**4** Draw in the arms with circles for the hands. Add a pistol.

**splat-a-fact!**
Pirates wore eye patches and headscarves.

**5** Draw in ragged trousers and add the feet.

# Pete the Plank

**1** Start by drawing in the head shape with a line for the headscarf.

**2** Add a mouth, an ear, eyebrows and dots for eyes. Draw in a knotted headscarf.

**3** Draw in the body. Add a belt and buckle.

**splat-a-fact!**
Pirates climbed the 'rigging' - ropes which controlled the mast.

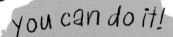

## you can do it!
Use brown felt-tip for the outlines and colour in with different felt-tips.

**4** Draw in ragged trousers and add the feet.

**5** Draw in the arms and hands. Add stripes to the trousers and top.

24

# sharkbait George

**1** Start with the head shape. Add a line for the headscarf.

**2** Draw in the knotted headscarf. Add an ear, mouth and an arrow-shaped closed eye.

**3** Add the ragged trousers.

**4** Draw in the arms, with one holding up a telescope.

## you can do it!

Use a felt-tip for the lines and then add colour with watercolour paints. Dab on more colour with a sponge to add texture.

## splat-a-fact!

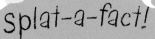

Telescopes helped pirates see into the distance.

**5** Draw in a waistcoat, buckle and belt. Add the legs, feet and a cannonball.

# Gunpowder Billy

**1** Start with an oval for the head. Add a line for the headscarf.

**2** Add a mouth, nose, hair and dots for the eyes. Draw in the knotted headscarf.

**3** Draw in the body shape.

### Splat-a-fact!

Pirates attacked enemy ships and kept much of the loot.

### you can do it!

Use a felt-tip for the lines. Add colour using chalky pastels. Use your fingers to blend the colours.

**4** Draw in the ragged trousers and add legs and feet.

**5** Draw in the arms, a treasure chest and a bag of loot.

# Captain Black

**1** Start with a square-shaped head. Add the shape of the hat.

**2** Draw in the nose, hair and beard.

**3** Draw in one eye, an eyepatch and mouth. Add a box-shaped body and an 'X' to the hat.

### you can do it!

Using wax crayons to create texture, paint over it with watercolour paint. Use felt-tip for the lines.

### Splat-a-fact!

Some pirates had hooks for hands.

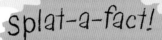

**5** Draw in sleeves with big cuffs. Add one hand with a sword and one with a hook.

**4** Draw in the jacket details: buttons and button holes. Add buckle. Draw in boots.

# Index

FREE APP!

Graphic Novels    Content

Page 16 of 58

Download our free iPhone and
iPad catalogue app. Search for
Salariya or Book House

Available on the App Store

# www.salariya.com
where books come to life!

SALARIYA

The Salariya Book Company is a UK-based independent
publisher of books for children which sells both domestically and
internationally. Through our imprints Book House, Scribblers and
Scribo we are dedicated to publishing books with real child
appeal, using innovative concepts, high-quality illustrations,
informative writing and, above all, humour to captivate the minds
of young people. With a mind for the environment, all of our
books are printed on paper from sustainable forests. Click the
links below to visit our imprints' websites, read our Book House
Blog or dive into a world of free interactive web books from the
best-selling 'You Wouldn't Want To Be...' series.

The Salariya Book Company,
25, Marlborough Place,
Brighton,
East Sussex
BN1 1UB
England
United Kingdom

Tel: 01273 603306
Fax: 01273 621619

rights - anne.murray@salariya.com
press - jamie.pitman@salariya.com
editorial - stephen.haynes@salariya.com
managing director - david@salariya.com

BOOK HOUSE    Scribo    Scribblers    FREE WEB BOOKS    SALARIYA RIGHTS

twitter  facebook  flickr

twitter
Get short, timely messages from Salariya Book Co...

facebook

Follow us on Facebook
and Twitter

www.youtube.com/user/BookHouse100

BOOK HOUSE
Knowledge is power

Book House - Some Selected Titles

Children's non-fiction and graphic novels

Scribo fiction

Fiction for children and teenagers

Scribblers
Bright Start
FREE WEB BOOK!

Free activities,
puzzles and web
books, with
information about
our books for
babies, toddlers
and pre-school

Dead?

FREE WEB BOOKS!

Four free web books

THE BOOK HOUSE
BLOG

The Book House blog -
competitions, giveaways
and current news